Southwest Desert Wildlife

Includes:

Southwest Desert Biomes

Habitats and Habits

Bird Activities

Mammal Activities

Reptile & Amphibian Activities

Invertebrate Activities

Wildlife Respect

Waterford Press

www.waterfordpress.com

Introduction

The American Southwest includes three major biomes—Sonoran Desert, Chihuahuan Desert and the Mohave Desert, which span Southern California, Arizona, southern Nevada, southern Utah and southern New Mexico.

A biome is a large region that has similar plants, animals and organisms that have adapted to the geography and climate of that area. A biome can have several ecosystems.

An ecosystem is a community of organisms that interact with each other and with their environment. Several ecosystems can exist within a biome. Ecosystems within the four major biomes of the Southwest include deserts; grasslands and shrublands; rivers, streams and wetlands; montane forests; pinyon-juniper woodlands; and forests.

A diverse range of animals live in the Southwest desert region, including spiders, scorpions, coyotes, bobcats, rattlesnakes, lizards, many species of birds and more.

Southwest Desert Biomes

Chihuahuan Desert
The Chihuahuan is the largest desert in North America. It covers parts of New Mexico and west Texas, extending far south into Mexico. It receives more rain than the Sonoran and Mohave Deserts, mostly during the summer monsoon thunderstorms. Resident wildlife includes the mule deer, jaguar and black-tailed prairie dog.

Sonoran Desert
The Sonoran Desert covers part of Arizona and California, extending south into Mexico. It is the hottest desert in both the United States and Mexico, and the only place in the world where the saguaro cactus grows. The Gila monster lives in the Sonoran, as do the desert centipede and diamondback rattlesnake.

Mojave Desert
The Mojave Desert spans parts of Nevada, Utah, Arizona, and a large portion of southeast California. Death Valley's Badwater Basin—the lowest point in North America at 282 feet below sea level—is located in the Mojave. The Joshua Tree, the Mojave's most recognizable plant, provides food and shelter for a number of mammals, birds, reptiles and insects. Other desert dwellers include the greater roadrunner, desert pupfish and desert hairy scorpion

Class Act

Animals can be sorted into categories based on certain characteristics. The system for sorting animals into categories is called taxonomy. Mammals, birds, fish, reptiles and amphibians belong to a class of animals called vertebrates. Vertebrates are animals with backbones. Invertebrates are another class of animals that do not have backbones (like insects, spiders, scorpions, centipedes and snails).

Draw a line between the animal and the class it belongs to.

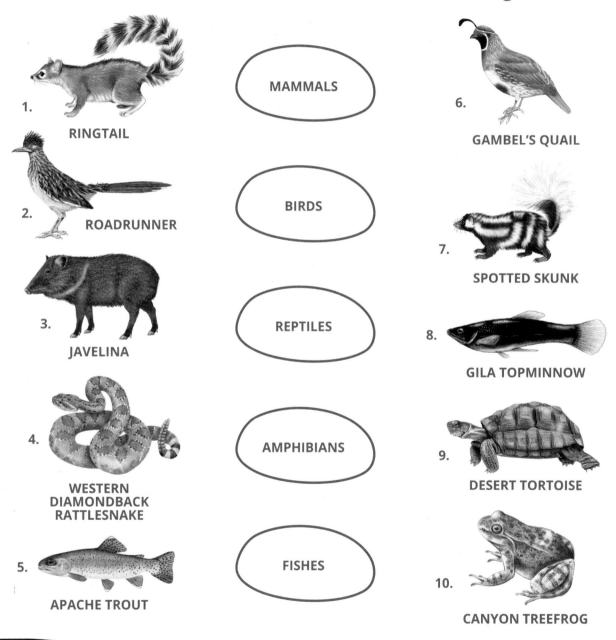

1. RINGTAIL

2. ROADRUNNER

3. JAVELINA

4. WESTERN DIAMONDBACK RATTLESNAKE

5. APACHE TROUT

MAMMALS

BIRDS

REPTILES

AMPHIBIANS

FISHES

6. GAMBEL'S QUAIL

7. SPOTTED SKUNK

8. GILA TOPMINNOW

9. DESERT TORTOISE

10. CANYON TREEFROG

You Are What You Eat

Herbivores eat mostly plants. Carnivores eat mostly animals. Omnivores eat plants and animals.

Draw a line between the desert animal and its diet.

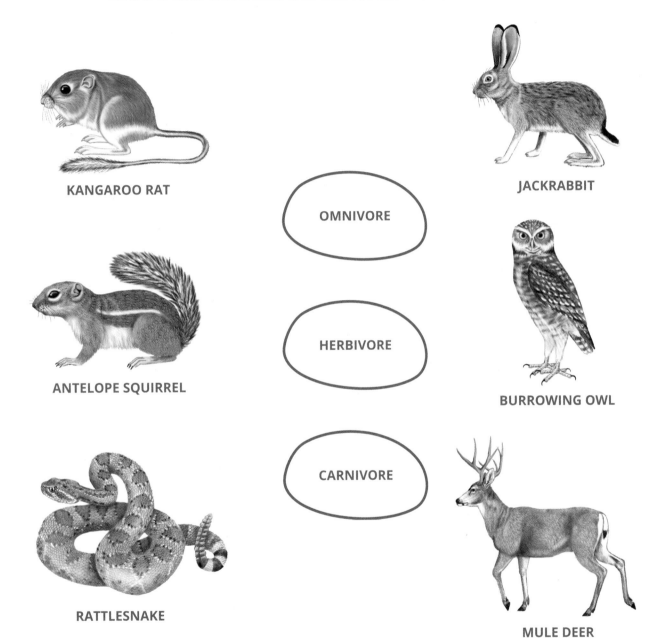

KANGAROO RAT

JACKRABBIT

OMNIVORE

HERBIVORE

CARNIVORE

ANTELOPE SQUIRREL

BURROWING OWL

RATTLESNAKE

MULE DEER

Food Chain

A food chain is the order in which animals feed on other plants or animals.

Producers – A producer takes the sun's energy and stores it as food.

Consumers – A consumer feeds on other living things to get energy. Consumers can include herbivores, carnivores and omnivores.

Decomposers – A decomposer consumes waste and dead organisms for energy.

Label each living organism below as a producer, consumer or decomposer.

MESQUITE

_____

COYOTE

_____

BARN OWL

_____

DUNG BEETLE

_____

ROADRUNNER

_____

BLUE GRAMA

_____

Find My Home

A habitat provides everything an animal needs for survival: food, shelter, water, the right temperature and protection from predators (animals who prey on other living things).

Draw a line between the animal and its habitat.

1.
DESERT BIGHORN SHEEP

2.
RATTLESNAKE

3.
BAT

4.
GILA WOODPECKER

(A)
I roost in rocky caves during the day and feed on insects at night.

(B)
I often drill holes high up on saguaro cacti where I make my nest and raise my young.

(C)
I live in rocky, mountainous areas where my hoofed feet allow me to climb with ease.

(D)
I rest in shady areas during the hot day and slither out at night to hunt.

Be An Artist

Draw this quail by copying it one square at a time.

Gambel's quail have a fancy head plume called a teardrop topknot. These ground-dwelling birds are common in rural and urban areas in the desert region. They have a distinctive four-note call—chi-ca-go-go—that is often heard throughout the day.

Color Key

8

Word Search

Some desert birds nest on the ground, while others nest in plants and trees. Like all animals, desert birds need water to survive. These clever birds stay in the shade when it's hot to avoid panting, which causes their bodies to lose water. They also get moisture from the foods they eat, like fruits, insects and other prey.

Find the names of these desert birds in the puzzle.

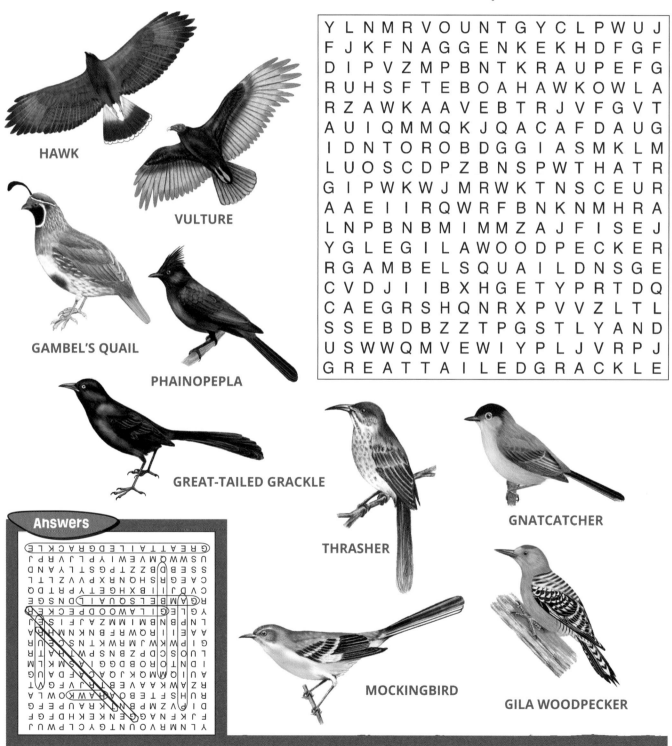

HAWK

VULTURE

GAMBEL'S QUAIL

PHAINOPEPLA

GREAT-TAILED GRACKLE

THRASHER

GNATCATCHER

MOCKINGBIRD

GILA WOODPECKER

```
Y L N M R V O U N T G Y C L P W U J
F J K F N A G G E N K E K H D F G F
D I P V Z M P B N T K R A U P E F G
R U H S F T E B O A H A W K O W L A
R Z A W K A A V E B T R J V F G V T
A U I Q M M Q K J Q A C A F D A U G
I D N T O R O B D G G I A S M K L M
L U O S C D P Z B N S P W T H A T R
G I P W K W J M R W K T N S C E U R
A A E I I R Q W R F B N K N M H R A
L N P B N B M I M M Z A J F I S E J
Y G L E G I L A W O O D P E C K E R
R G A M B E L S Q U A I L D N S G E
C V D J I I B X H G E T Y P R T D Q
C A E G R S H Q N R X P V V Z L T L
S S E B D B Z Z T P G S T L Y A N D
U S W W Q M V E W I Y P L J V R P J
G R E A T T A I L E D G R A C K L E
```

Answers

9

Maze

Roadrunners are quick enough to catch rattlesnakes! They spend most of their time on the ground hunting and can run at speeds of up to 20 mph (32 kph)—almost twice as fast as the average human!

Help this roadrunner find its prey.

ENTER

Make Words

The **burrowing owl** is a tiny long-legged owl found in deserts, grasslands and rangelands. It spends most of its time on the ground and rarely flies. Unlike most owls, it nests in underground burrows and is active during the day. It is often seen standing on the ground near the entrance to its burrow.

How many words can you make from the letters in its name?

Answers

Possible answers include: big, bingo, blur, boo, bow, bowl, bring, brow, brown, burl, burr, gin, glow, gown, ling, lingo, lob, low, lowing, now, orb, own, rib, rig, ring, rob, row, rub, wig, wing, woo, wool, wow, wring, wrong, wrung

Maze

Black-chinned hummingbirds are common throughout southwestern deserts. In cooler weather, these tiny birds may consume three times their body weight in nectar in one day. Their wings beat so fast—50 times per second—they make a humming sound that can be easily heard when they fly by. They are the only birds capable of flying backwards.

Help this hummingbird find its nectar source.

ENTER

Word Search

Birds of prey hunt rodents, rabbits, lizards, fish and even other birds. They have keen vision, strong talons and hooked beaks to help them catch food. Birds of prey are common in the desert and can be found in almost every kind of habitat.

Find the names of these birds of prey in the puzzle.

NORTHERN HARRIER

FERRUGINOUS HAWK

RED-TAILED HAWK

HARRIS'S HAWK

BLACK VULTURE

TURKEY VULTURE

ELF OWL

GREAT HORNED OWL

```
Z V S Q T X G C I R H P C F Q N S
T D J M X X K X T D O V Y Z B Q V
U R I J F X B V D V P V W A U D M
N U Y Z Q X U G A L W L Z C R T A
B A H A Q J A Q D K D I G B R U P
G R E A T H O R N E D O W L O R G
D F E R R U G I N O U S H A W K O
X Y K D P R P B E C V B A C I E L
O B E C Z X I K E T Z D Q K N Y D
Z M P L U I X S P Y J A A V G V E
J C X F F W A H S L Y S Z U O U N
V L R O G O T I R H Z S E L W L E
B Y C K N M W H X F A A A T L T A
X Y Y C F J R L E H K W J U S U G
R E D T A I L E D H A W K R U R L
N O R T H E R N H A R R I E R E E
Y C P R K N U M E Y Z P H B P Z A
```

Answers

Y C P R K N U M E Y Z P H B P Z A
N O R T H E R N H A R R I E R E E
R E D T A I L E D H A W K R U R L
X Y Y C F J R L E H K W J U S U G
B Y C K N M W H X F A A A T L T A
V L R O G O T I R H Z S E L W L E
J C X F F W A H S L Y S Z U O U N
Z M P L U I X S P Y J A A V G V E
O B E C Z X I K E T Z D Q K N Y D
X Y K D P R P B E C V B A C I E L
D F E R R U G I N O U S H A W K O
G R E A T H O R N E D O W L O R G
B A H A Q J A Q D K D I G B R U P
N U Y Z Q X U G A L W L Z C R T A
U R I J F X B V D V P V W A U D M
T D J M X X K X T D O V Y Z B Q V
Z V S Q T X G C I R H P C F Q N S

Name Scramble

Mammals give birth to live young that feed on milk from their mother. These animals have fur or hair, and use their nose, mouth and lungs to breathe air. Some desert mammals burrow underground to escape the heat. Others use shrubs and plants for shelter.

Unscramble the letters to form the names of these desert animals.

1. TOOEYC

2. EDRE

3. ONTNUOAILINM

4. OROATWD

5. TBA

6. QSULIRER

7. NOCRCAO

8. KKSUN

Make Words

The **antelope squirrel** is especially adapted to live in the desert. The soles of its feet are heavily furred to protect its feet from the hot ground. It also has the unique habit of carrying its tail arched over its back like a sunshade when it moves about in the midday sun.

How many words can you make from the letters in its name?

_____   _____

_____   _____

_____   _____

_____   _____

_____   _____

_____   _____

_____   _____

_____   _____

_____   _____

_____   _____

_____   _____

Answers

Possible answers include: ant, ape, art, aspen, aunt, eat, eel, equal, ill, lane, late, lean, leap, pant, pat, peel, pet, pole, pose, post, quill, quit, quote, rant, rat, ripe, roll, rope, rose, squirt, soap, sell, tail, tale, tall, tape, use

Connect The Dots

This North American carnivore is name for its short, black-tipped, stubby tail. It inhabits a variety of habitats throughout the U.S. and is common in the desert region. Its hind legs are longer than its front legs so it walks with a bobbing motion.

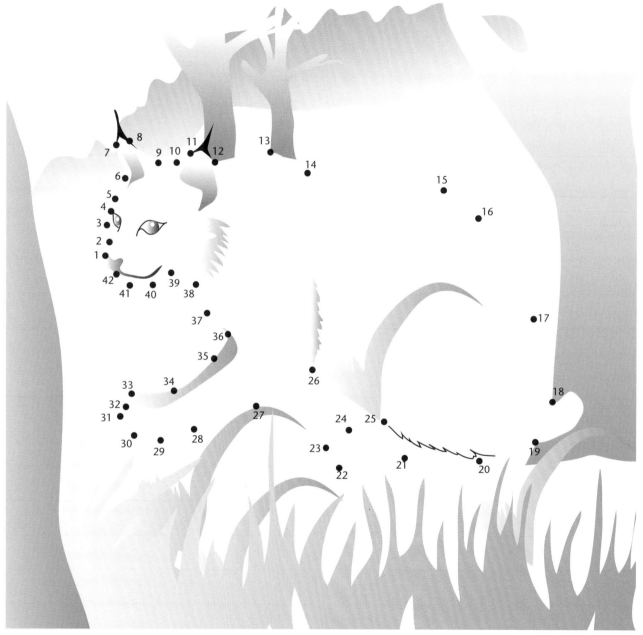

Bonus question:
What am I?

Maze

Jackrabbits are not really rabbits—they are hares! Unlike rabbits, hares are born in nests above the ground. A jackrabbit depends on its speed to avoid predators. If it senses a predator nearby it will spring up and leap away in a zigzag pattern. Jackrabbits can run 35 to 40 miles per hour!

Help the jackrabbit avoid its predators.

Animal Tracks

Studying tracks is an easy way to discover the kinds of mammals found in an area.

Draw a line between the desert mammal and its tracks.

COYOTE

1.

2.

3.

4.

5.

6.

DEER MOUSE

MULE DEER

GROUND SQUIRREL

SPOTTED SKUNK

GRAY FOX

Answers

1. Coyote
2. Deer Mouse
3. Spotted Skunk
4. Gray Fox
5. Mule Deer
6. Ground Squirrel

Origami

The **mountain lion** and **bobcat** are two species of wild cats found in the deserts of the American Southwest. Mountain lions rest in secluded canyons or rocky outcrops with thick cover. Bobcats hunt on the ground but will climb trees for safety. Both animals are secretive and not often seen by humans.

Starting with a square piece of paper, follow the folding instructions to make a cat's face. Decorate it to look like a bobcat or mountain lion.

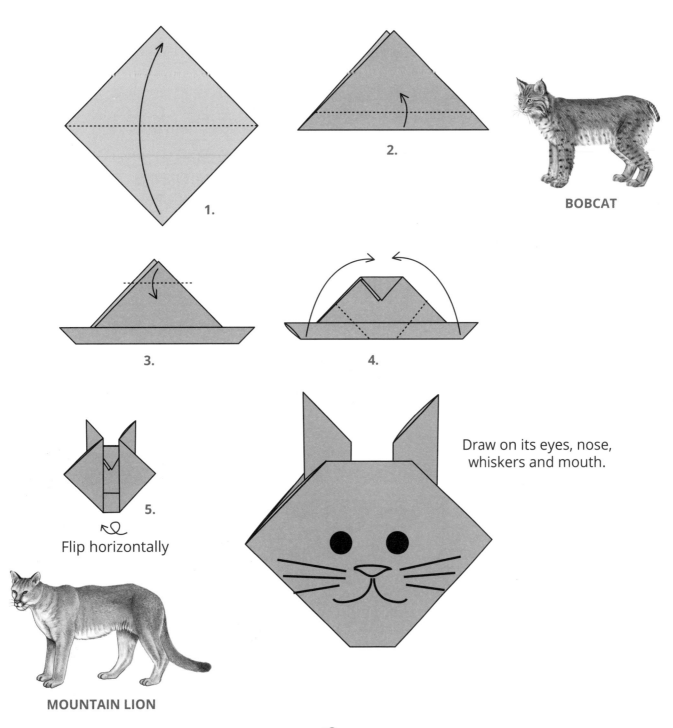

1.

2.

BOBCAT

3.

4.

5.

Flip horizontally

Draw on its eyes, nose, whiskers and mouth.

MOUNTAIN LION

Word Search

The desert landscape includes many habitats, from mountains and valleys to wetlands and forests—and reptiles are found in all of them.

Find the names of these reptiles in the puzzle.

GILA MONSTER

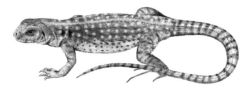

IGUANA

FENCE LIZARD

GECKO

```
L X D C H U C K W A L L A I I A
I M M B F Y K U I K B O F F H Y
S A F H U G U K W I M P E F W V
F T D K K O Q A C L E S N H C L
H O R N E D L I Z A R D C G O N
M R C Z G P P G G D M F E I R R
Q T I D X U D M E U V F L M A K
U O T M T L Z V D S A N I I L A
B I X W G K I T W Y Q N Z S S M
L S L O E Q R U G I U G A X N Z
R E G I L A M O N S T E R O A T
K H K E Z U V K R H J W D O K Q
O A G U C F C C A Z F E K W E B
B P Z M T K Q U E V O J Q I V F
M A U M O S O E K X L L Y N R Y
X C D U Q J F T S Y L Z W I F V
```

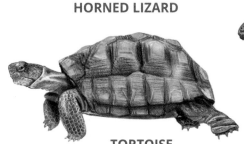

HORNED LIZARD

CHUCKWALLA

TORTOISE

CORAL SNAKE

Answers

20

Make Words

The **Gila monster** is one of only two known dangerously venomous lizards in the world. Its name comes from the Gila River basin, where it was first discovered. It usually hides underground or under rocks and eats small mammals, lizards and birds.

How many words can you make from the letters in its name?

_____

_____

_____

_____

_____

_____

_____

_____

_____

_____

_____

_____

_____

_____

_____

_____

Be An Artist

Draw this horned lizard by copying it one square at a time.

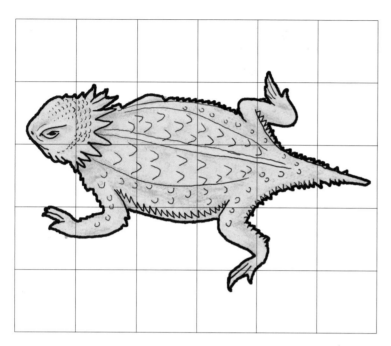

The **horned lizard** is often incorrectly called a horned frog. This reptile lives in sandy areas in the desert. It is very hard to spot because it blends in perfectly with the ground, something that helps it to sneak up on ants and other prey. When threatened, it has the unusual behavior of squirting blood out of its eye sockets.

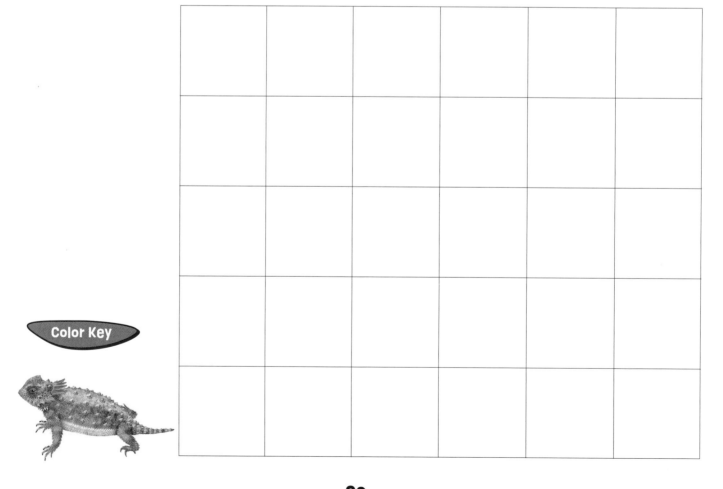

Color Key

Connect the Dots

Amphibians are smooth-skinned, limbed vertebrates that live in moist habitats and breathe through lungs, skin, gills or a combination of all three. While many spend much of their lives on land, they still depend on a watery environment to complete their life cycle. Most reproduce by laying eggs in or near water. The young hatch as swimming larvae that breathe through gills. After a short developmental period, the larvae metamorphose into young adults with lungs and legs.

I am a warty amphibian. My name rhymes with "load."
Follow the numbers to connect the dots and draw the mystery amphibian.

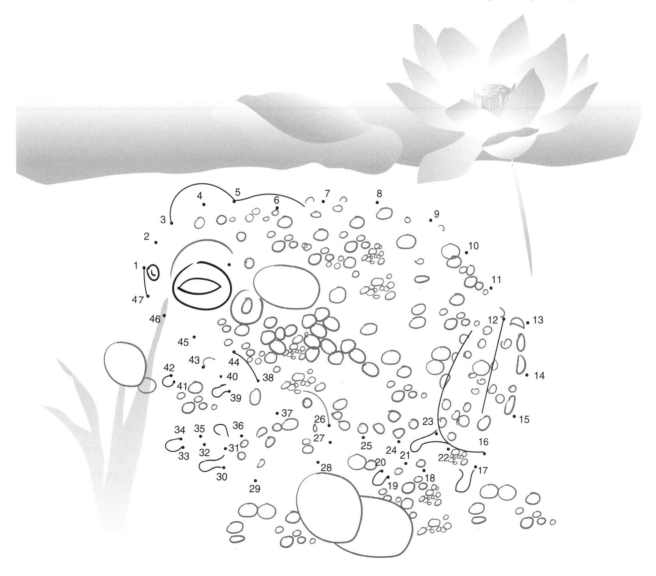

Who am I?

Answers

Crossword

Snakes play a very important role in the ecosystem. They are typically in the middle of the food web, being both predator and prey. Their predators are birds of prey, coyotes, raccoons, opossums as well as feral cats and hogs. As predators, and depending on their size and environment, snakes eat rodents, worms, insects, fish, frogs, toads, bird eggs and nestlings.

Use the clues about snakes to solve the puzzle.

Across

3. To help recognize this venous snake, people use this rhyme "Red on yellow can kill a fellow."
5. It feeds on rodents and is valued for controlling the spread of mice by eating them.
7. Its tail looks like a braided whip.
8. This snake has a pointed upturned snout, which it uses to burrow into the ground in search of toads.

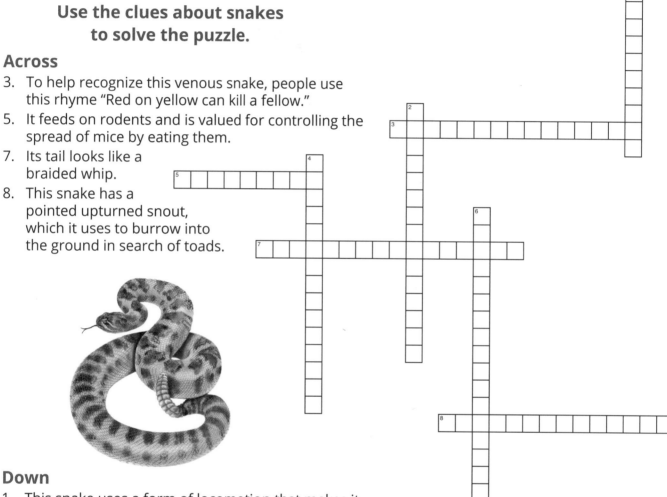

Down

1. This snake uses a form of locomotion that makes it appear to move sideways.
2. It is also often called a Black Snake.
4. Immune to rattlesnake venom, it commonly feeds on rattlesnake.
6. One of the most dangerous, venomous snakes living in the deserts of the southwestern US and central Mexico.

Origami

The snake is a fascinating animal. It does not have an outside ear like humans do, but it does have an inner ear that allows it to hear some sounds and to pick up vibrations from the ground. Instead of a nose, it uses its tongue and a special organ on the roof of its mouth to "smell" things in its environment.

Starting with a square piece of paper, follow the simple folding instructions below to create this snake.

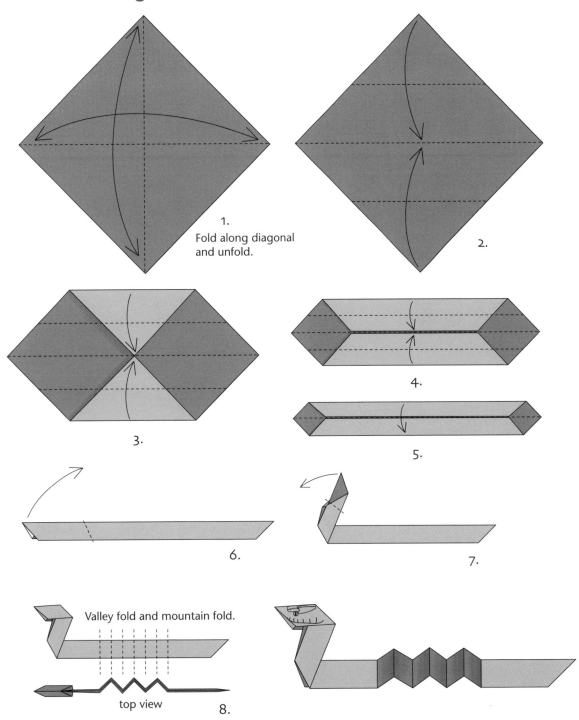

1. Fold along diagonal and unfold.

2.

3.

4.

5.

6.

7.

8. Valley fold and mountain fold.

top view

Who Am I?

Many invertebrates live in the desert, including insects, spiders and scorpions. Arthropods are invertebrates with jointed legs and an exoskeleton (hard outside covering).

Name the invertebrates below.

1. I am a tiny aggressive red ant found all over desert areas. I'm named for the pain you feel when I bite you.

4. I am a common desert creature with a stinger on my tail. Don't forget to shake your boots out in the morning!

2. I am a poisonous spider that hides in debris piles and old buildings. I'm named after my habit of eating my mate.

5. I am a large, hairy desert spider with big fangs.

3. I am the industrious state insect of Utah.

Butterflies and Moths

The two groups differ in several ways:

Butterflies	Moths
• Active by day	• Active at night
• Brightly colored	• Most are dull colored
• Thin body	• Stout body
• Rests with wings held erect over its back	• Rests with wings folded, tent-like, over its back
• Antennae are thin and thickened at the tip	• Antennae are usually thicker and often feathery

All butterflies and moths have a complex life cycle consisting of four developmental stages.

1. Eggs
2. Caterpillars (larvae)
3. Pupae (chrysalis/ cocoon)
4. Adult

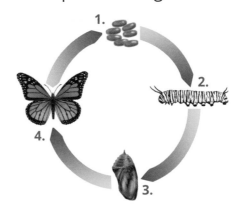

Attracting Butterflies to Your Yard

Food – Almost all butterfly caterpillars eat plants; adult butterflies feed almost only on plant nectar. Your library or local garden shop will have information on which plants attract which species.

Water – Soak the soil in your garden or sandy areas to create puddles. These provide a source of water and minerals.

Rocks – Put large flat rocks in sunny areas. Butterflies will gather there to spread their wings and warm up.

Brush – Small brush piles and hollow logs provide ideal places for butterflies to lay their eggs and hibernate over the winter.

Connect the Dots

Butterflies can be found in almost all kinds of habitats, including deserts. In fact, there are more than 250 species in the Sonoran Desert alone!

Draw this butterfly as it feeds on nectar from a flowering desert plant.

Word Search

Find the names of these desert plants.

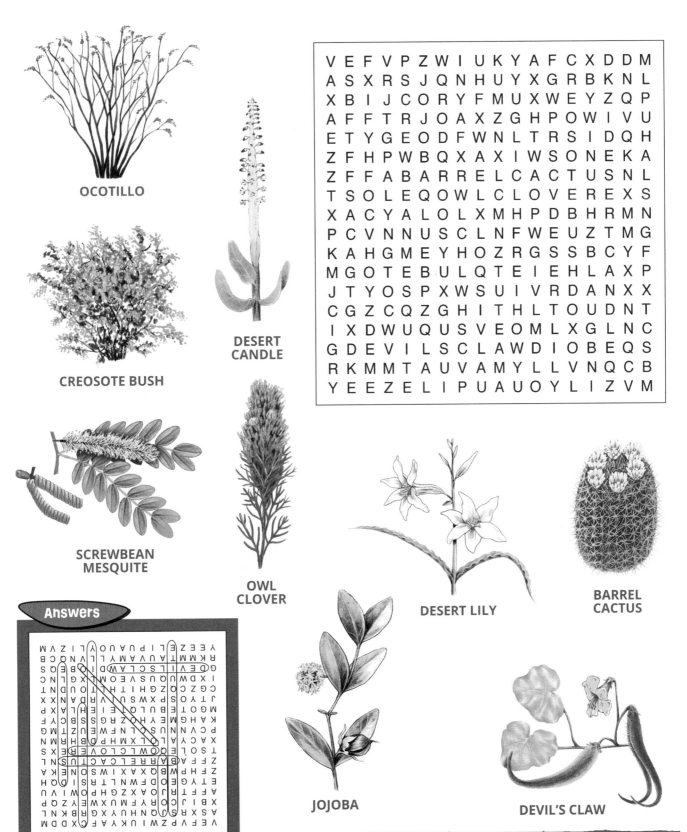

OCOTILLO

CREOSOTE BUSH

DESERT CANDLE

SCREWBEAN MESQUITE

OWL CLOVER

DESERT LILY

BARREL CACTUS

Answers

JOJOBA

DEVIL'S CLAW

The word search grid:

```
V E F V P Z W I U K Y A F C X D D M
A S X R S J Q N H U Y X G R B K N L
X B I J C O R Y F M U X W E Y Z Q P
A F F T R J O A X Z G H P O W I V U
E T Y G E O D F W N L T R S I D Q H
Z F H P W B Q X A X I W S O N E K A
Z F F A B A R R E L C A C T U S N L
T S O L E Q O W L C L O V E R E X S
X A C Y A L O L X M H P D B H R M N
P C V N N U S C L N F W E U Z T M G
K A H G M E Y H O Z R G S S B C Y F
M G O T E B U L Q T E I E H L A X P
J T Y O S P X W S U I V R D A N X X
C G Z C Q Z G H I T H L T O U D N T
I X D W U Q U S V E O M L X G L N C
G D E V I L S C L A W D I O B E Q S
R K M M T A U V A M Y L L V N Q C B
Y E E Z E L I P U A U O Y L I Z V M
```

29

Name Match

The cactus is a desert plant that stores water in order to survive. There are almost 2,000 species of cacti in the world.

Draw a line between each Southwest desert cactus and its name.

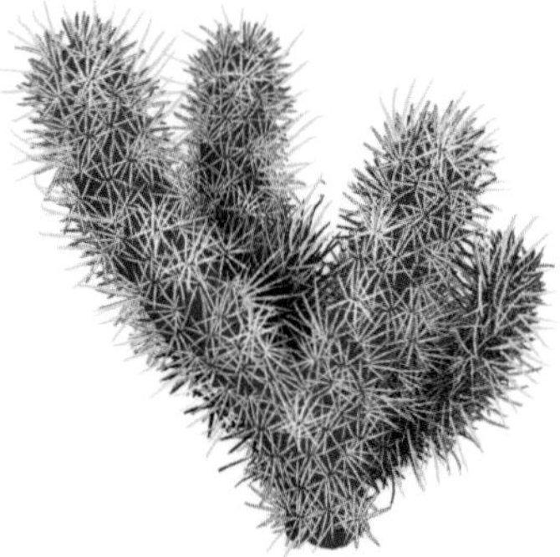

1.

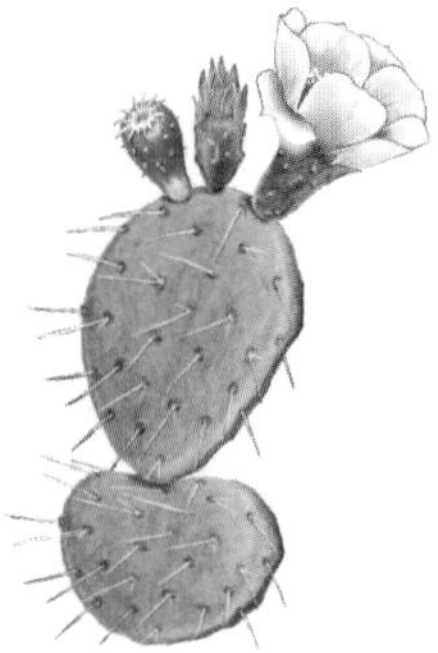

2.

3.

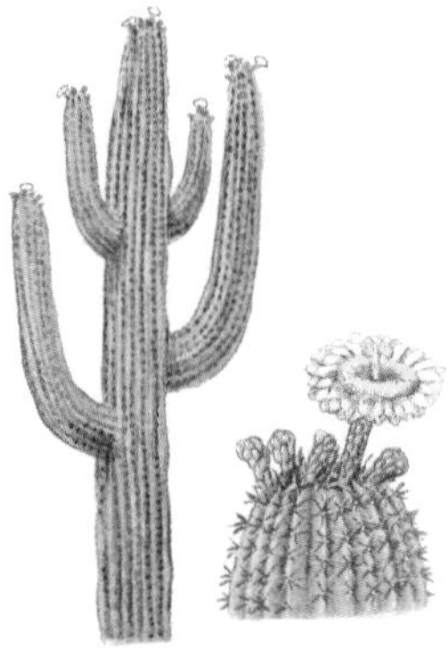

HEDGEHOG CACTUS

SAGUARO

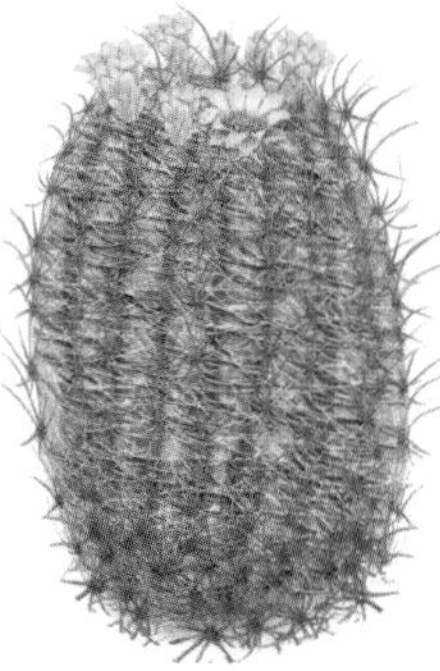

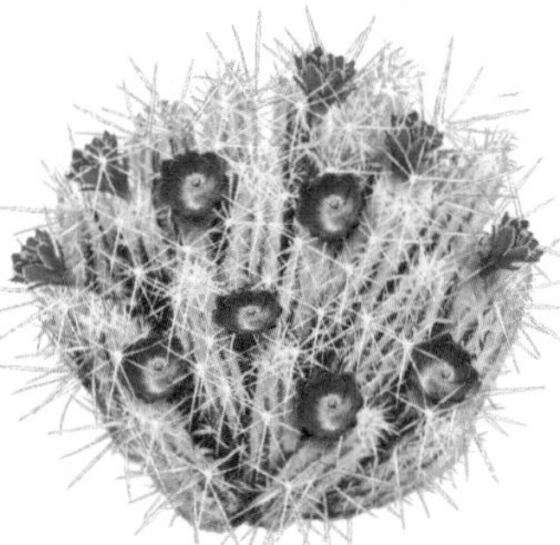

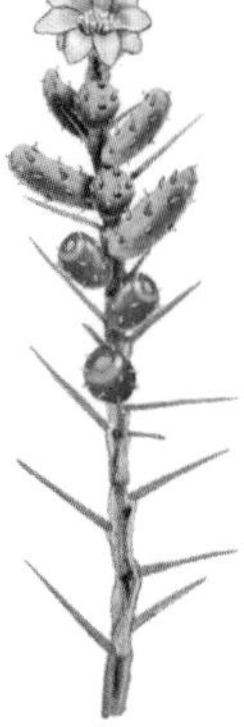

PRICKLY PEAR

TEDDY-BEAR CHOLLA

CHRISTMAS CACTUS

BARREL CACTUS

4.

5.

6.

Answers

1. Prickly Pear
2. Teddy-bear Cholla
3. Saguaro
4. Barrel Cactus
5. Hedgehog Cactus
6. Christmas Cactus

Color Me

The saguaro cactus grows only in the Sonoran Desert. It can grow as tall as 50 feet and live to over 150 years. The giant saguaro provides shelter and food for a lot of desert wildlife.

Color the picture of the saguaro cactus and the cactus wren that lives or rests there.

Color Key

Wildlife Respect

In wild spaces, humans are the visitors. We are lucky to be able to observe animals in their natural habitats. Along with that privilege, comes a responsibility to respect the animals we see, as well as their homes. The best way to learn about wildlife is by quietly watching. Though the possibility of getting a better look—or a better photo—can be tempting, getting too close can be stressful to a wild animal.

Here are some ways you can help reduce the number of disruptive human encounters that wild animals experience:

1. Know the site before you go.
2. When taking photos, do not use a flash, which can disturb animals.
3. Give animals room to move and act naturally.
4. Visit after breakfast and before dinner when wild animals are less active.
5. Do not touch or disturb the animals.
6. Do not feed the animals.
7. Store your food and take your trash with you.
8. Read and respect signs.
9. Do not make quick movements or loud noises.
10. Report any encounters with dangerous animals.